Spelling Connections

J. Richard Gentry, Ph.D.

K

Zaner-Bloser

Author

J. Richard Gentry, Ph.D.

Illustrations: Yvette Banek: pp. 13–14, 29–30, 47–48; Chi Chung: pp. 23–24, 41–42; Marion Eldridge: pp. 39–40; Kate Flanagan: pp. 11–12, 31–32, 49–50; Patrick Girouard: pp. 33–34; Dennis Hockerman: pp. 35–36; Sharon Holm: pp. 17–18, 27–28, 45–46; Illustrated Alaskan Moose: pp. 5–6, 55–56; Ron Lieser: pp. 15–16, 53–54; Tammie Lyon: pp. 25–26, 43–44; Ben Mahan: pp. 7–8, 21–22; Steve McInturff: pp. 37–38; Susan Nethery: pp. 9–10, 19–20; John Nez: pp. 51–52

ISBN 978-1-4531-1722-4

ZB Code 16

Zaner-Bloser, Inc.
1-800-421-3018
www.zaner-bloser.com
Printed in the United States of America   3 4 5 6 7   997   21 20 19 18 17

Contents

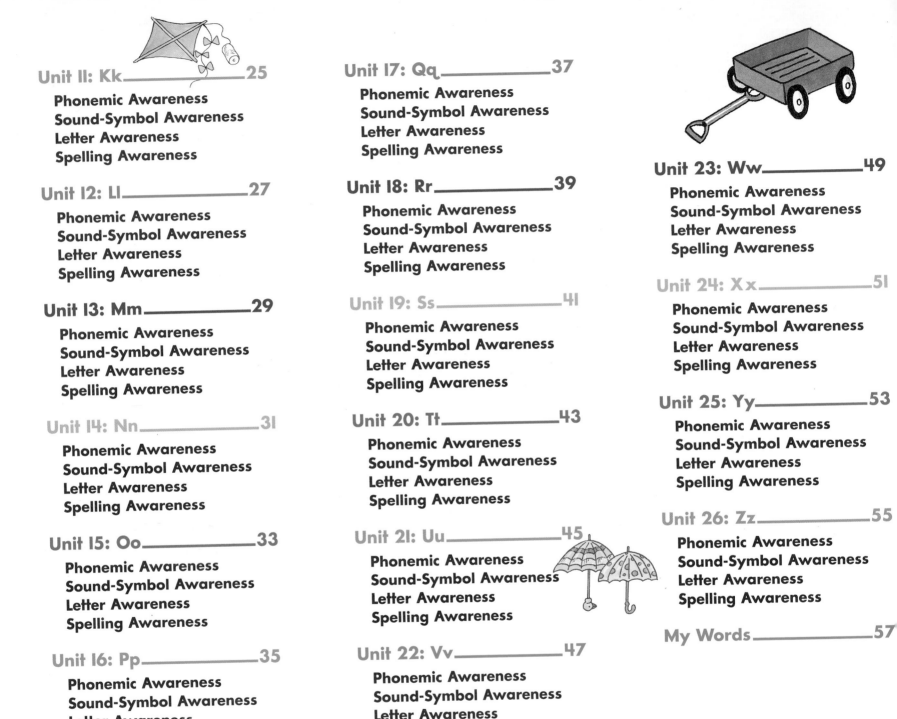

Name _____

Phonemic Awareness

● Say the name of each picture.
   Circle the pictures that begin with the same sound as **apple**.

Sound-Symbol Awareness

★ Read the name of each picture.
   Circle each **a**.

apple   and   ants

To the Teacher
Help children recognize the **short a** sound as they name each picture. Associate this sound with the letters **Aa**.

Letter Awareness

▲ Trace. Practice.

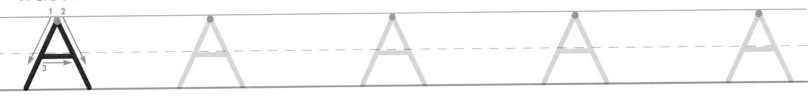

Spelling Awareness

■ Write **a** to complete each spelling.

 ·nts    ·nd

 ·pple    f·n

School/Home
This page provides practice with the sound of **short a**. Help your child name the pictures and practice writing the letters.

Name _____

Bb

● Say the name of each picture.
Circle the pictures that begin with the same sound as **bus**.

Sound-Symbol Awareness

★ Say the name of each picture as you read.
Circle each **b**.

This bag is for the little

 boy.

 To the Teacher
Help children recognize the /b/ sound as they name each picture. Associate this sound with the letters **Bb**.

▲ Trace. Practice.

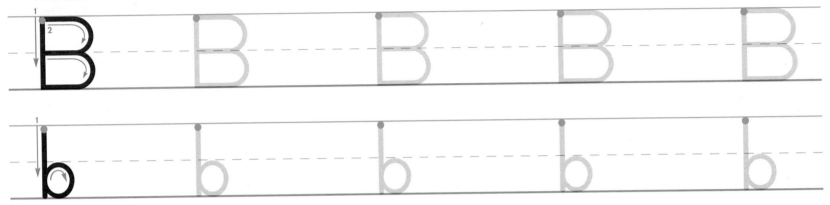

Spelling Awareness

■ Write **b** to complete each spelling.

 us

 ig

 ee

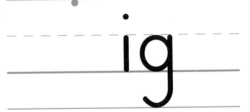 at

School/Home
This page provides practice with the sound of initial **Bb**. Help your child name the pictures and practice writing the letters.

Name

Phonemic Awareness

● Say the name of each picture.
Circle the pictures that begin with the same sound as  **cup**.

Sound-Symbol Awareness

★ Read the name of each picture.
Circle each **c**.

cup

cows

cat

 To the Teacher
Help children recognize the **/k/** sound as they name each picture. Associate this sound with the letters **Cc**.

9

▲ Trace. Practice.

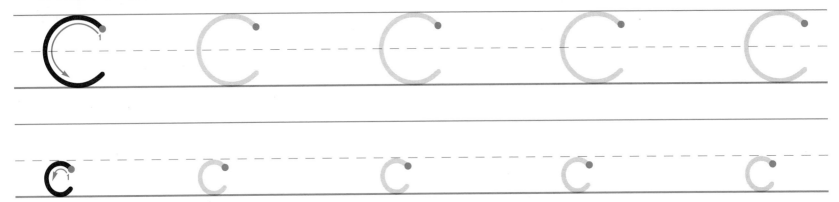

Spelling Awareness

■ Write **c** to complete each spelling.

 ows

 an

 up

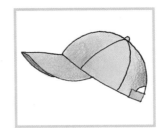 ap

School/Home
This page provides practice with the **/k/** sound of **Cc**. Help your child name the pictures and practice writing the letters.

Name

Dd

● Say the name of each picture.
Circle the pictures that begin with the same sound as **duck**.

Sound-Symbol Awareness

★ Say the name of each picture as you read.
Circle each **d**.

The  dish waved to
the  dog.

To the Teacher
Help children recognize the **/d/** sound as they name each picture. Associate this sound with the letters **Dd**.

▲ Trace. Practice.

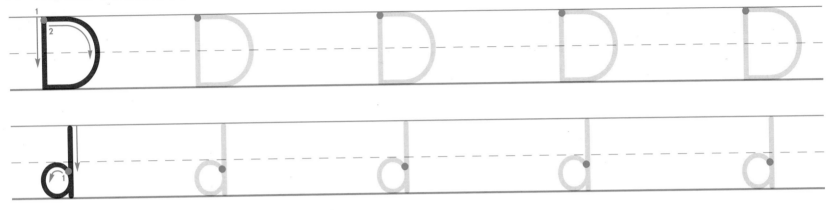

Spelling Awareness

■ Write **d** to complete each spelling.

 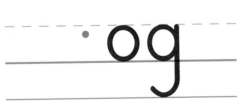

School/Home
This page provides practice with the sound of initial **Dd**. Help your child name the pictures and practice writing the letters.

Name _____

Phonemic Awareness

● Say the name of each picture.
Circle the pictures that begin with the same sound as  **elf**.

Sound-Symbol Awareness

★ Say the name of each picture as you read.
Circle each **e**.

 Meg likes a regular

 egg!

To the Teacher
Help children recognize the **short e** sound as they name each picture. Associate this sound with the letters **Ee**.

Letter Awareness

▲ Trace. Practice.

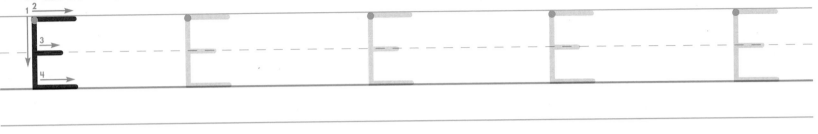

Spelling Awareness

■ Write **e** to complete each spelling.

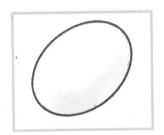  gg

 M  g

  lf

 n  t

School/Home
This page provides practice with the sound of **short e**. Help your child name the pictures and practice writing the letters.

Phonemic Awareness

● Say the name of each picture.
Circle the pictures that begin with the same sound as 🌾 **fence**.

Sound-Symbol Awareness

★ Say the name of the picture as you read.
Circle each **F** and **f**.

Fee, fi, fo, fum, see my finger, see my thumb.

To the Teacher
Help children recognize the **/f/** sound as they name each picture. Associate this sound with the letters **Ff**.

▲ Trace. Practice.

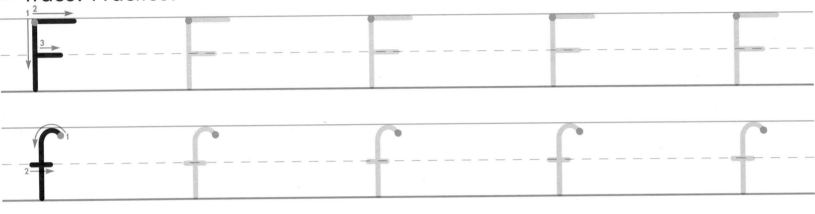

Spelling Awareness

■ Write **f** to complete each spelling.

  inger

  ly

  ish

 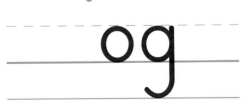 og

School/Home
This page provides practice with the sound of initial **Ff**. Help your child name the pictures and practice writing the letters.

Name _____

Gg

● Say the name of each picture.
Circle the pictures that begin with the same sound as  **guitar**.

 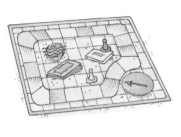  

Sound-Symbol Awareness

★ Read the name of each picture.
Circle each **g**.

goats

girls

geese

To the Teacher
Help children recognize the **/g/** sound as they name each picture. Associate this sound with the letters **Gg**.

▲ Trace. Practice.

Spelling Awareness

■ Write **g** to complete each spelling.

  irls

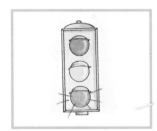  o

  ate

  ot

School/Home
This page provides practice with the sound of initial **Gg**. Help your child name the pictures and practice writing the letters.

Name

Phonemic Awareness

● Say the name of each picture.
Circle the pictures that begin with the same sound as **heart**.

Sound-Symbol Awareness

★ Say the name of each picture as you read.
Circle each **h**.

A hill is a house for an ant.

To the Teacher
Help children recognize the **/h/** sound as they name each picture. Associate this sound with the letters **Hh**.

Letter Awareness

▲ Trace. Practice.

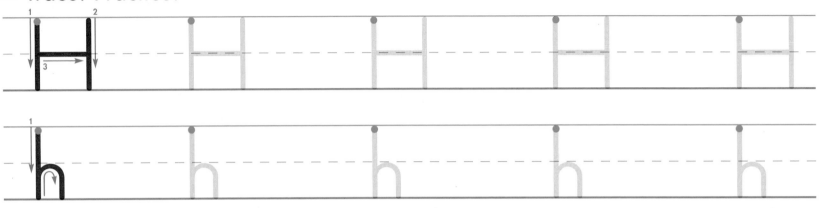

Spelling Awareness

■ Write **h** to complete each spelling.

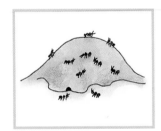 

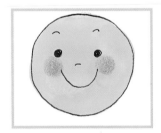 appy

 and

School/Home
This page provides practice with the sound of initial **Hh**. Help your child name the pictures and practice writing the letters.

Name

Phonemic Awareness

● Say the name of each picture.
Circle the pictures that begin with the same sound as  **igloo**.

Sound-Symbol Awareness

★ Read the name of each picture.
Circle each **i**.

in   ill   inch

To the Teacher
Help children recognize the **short i** sound as they name each picture. Associate this sound with the letters **Ii**.

▲ Trace. Practice.

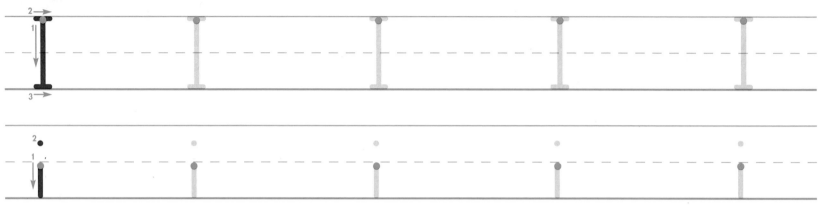

Spelling Awareness

■ Write **i** to complete each spelling.

      p · n

   · n

      · nk

      p · g

School/Home
This page provides practice with the sound of **short i**. Help your child name the pictures and practice writing the letters.

Name

Jj

- Say the name of each picture.
  Circle the pictures that begin with the same sound as **jar**.

Sound-Symbol Awareness

★ Say the name of each picture as you read.
  Circle each **J** and **j**.

 Jack   jump over
the candlestick.

To the Teacher
Help children recognize the **/j/** sound as they name each picture. Associate this sound with the letters **Jj**.

23

▲ Trace. Practice.

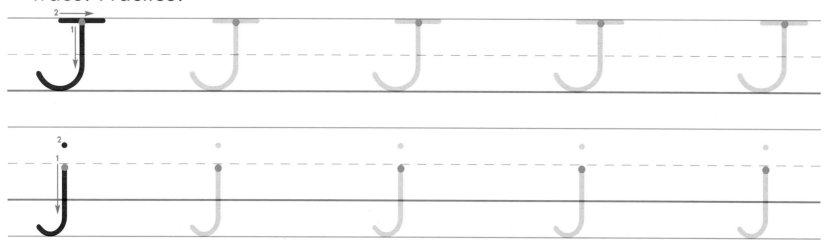

Spelling Awareness

■ Write **j** to complete each spelling.

 School/Home
This page provides practice with the sound of initial **Jj**. Help your child name the pictures and practice writing the letters.

Name _____

Phonemic Awareness

● Say the name of each picture.
Circle the pictures that begin with the same sound as **kite**.

Sound-Symbol Awareness

★ Read the name of each picture.
Circle each **k**.

key   kitten   kettle

To the Teacher
Help children recognize the **/k/** sound as they name each picture. Associate this sound with the letters **Kk**.

25

Letter Awareness

▲ Trace. Practice.

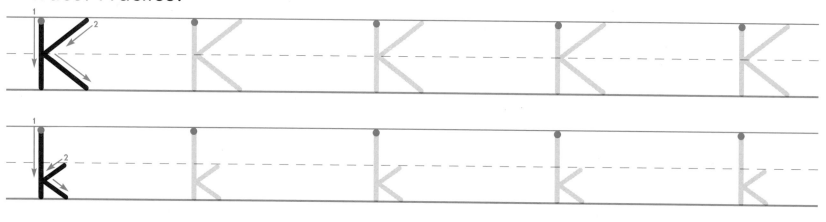

Spelling Awareness

■ Write **k** to complete each spelling.

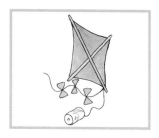  ite

  eep

  ey

  ing

School/Home
This page provides practice with the sound of initial **Kk**. Help your child name the pictures and practice writing the letters.

Phonemic Awareness

● Say the name of each picture.
Circle the pictures that begin with the same sound as **ladder**.

Sound-Symbol Awareness

★ Say the name of each picture as you read.
Circle each **l**.

My lazy little alligator lies on my lap.

To the Teacher
Help children recognize the /l/ sound as they name each picture. Associate this sound with the letters **Ll**.

▲ Trace. Practice.

Spelling Awareness

■ Write **l** to complete each spelling.

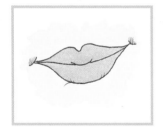  ips

 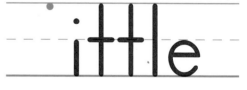 ittle

  ock

 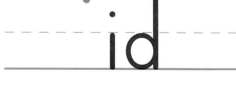 id

School/Home
This page provides practice with the sound of initial **Ll**. Help your child name the pictures and practice writing the letters.

Name

● Say the name of each picture.
Circle the pictures that begin with the same sound as **mop**.

★ Say the name of each picture as you read.
Circle each **m**.

Do you know the

 muffin  man?

To the Teacher
Help children recognize the /m/ sound as they name each picture. Associate this sound with the letters **Mm**.

▲ Trace. Practice.

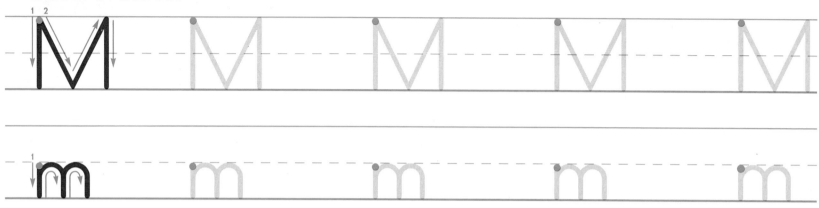

Spelling Awareness

■ Write **m** to complete each spelling.

  ud

  ap

  ilk

  an

School/Home
This page provides practice with the sound of initial **Mm**. Help your child name the pictures and practice writing the letters.

● Say the name of each picture.
Circle the pictures that begin with the same sound as **nest**.

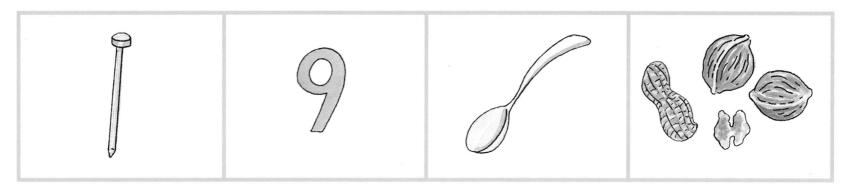

★ Read the name of each picture.
Circle each **n**.

nuts   noodles   nest

To the Teacher
Help children recognize the **/n/** sound as they name each picture. Associate this sound with the letters **Nn**.

31

▲ Trace. Practice.

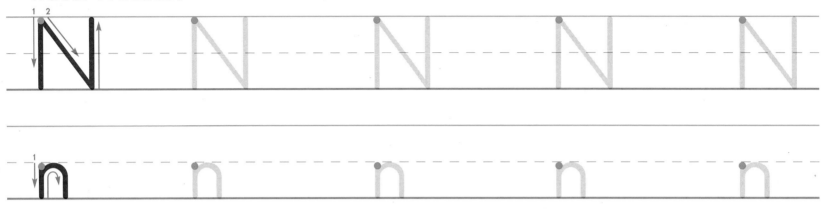

Spelling Awareness

■ Write **n** to complete each spelling.

  ail

  o

  et

  ine

School/Home
This page provides practice with the sound of initial **Nn**. Help your child name the pictures and practice writing the letters.

Name

Phonemic Awareness

● Say the name of each picture.
Circle the pictures that begin with the same sound as **octopus**.

Sound-Symbol Awareness

★ Read the name of each picture.
Circle each **o**.

owl

ox

on

To the Teacher
Help children recognize the **short o** sound as they name each picture. Associate this sound with the letters **Oo**.

33

Letter Awareness

▲ Trace. Practice.

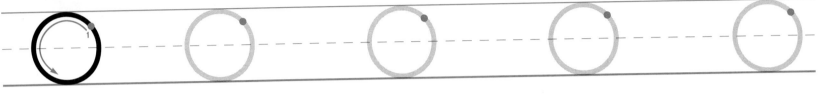

Spelling Awareness

■ Write **o** to complete each spelling.

   _ x

   _ ff

   _ n

   d _ ck

School/Home
This page provides practice with the sound of **short o**. Help your child name the pictures and practice writing the letters.

Pp

Phonemic Awareness

● Say the name of each picture.
Circle the pictures that begin with the same sound as **pencil**.

Sound-Symbol Awareness

★ Say the name of each picture as you read.
Circle each **P** and **p**.

Pop a 🫘 pancake in the 🍳 pan.

To the Teacher
Help children recognize the **/p/** sound as they name each picture. Associate this sound with the letters **Pp**.

▲ Trace. Practice.

P P P P P

p p p p p

Spelling Awareness

■ Write **p** to complete each spelling.

 ig

 lay

 eas

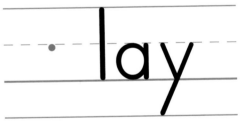 en

School/Home
This page provides practice with the sound of initial **Pp**. Help your child name the pictures and practice writing the letters.

Phonemic Awareness

● Say the name of each picture.
Circle the pictures that begin with the same sound as  **queen**.

Sound-Symbol Awareness

★ Read the name of each picture.
Circle each **q**.

queen

quilt

Quack, quack!

quack

 To the Teacher
Help children recognize the **/kw/** sound as they name each picture. Associate this sound with the letters **Qu** and **qu**.

Letter Awareness

▲ Trace. Practice.

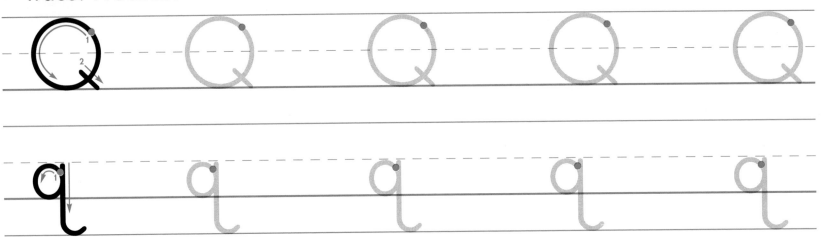

Spelling Awareness

■ Write **q** to complete each spelling.

ueen   uiet

uilt   uack

School/Home
This page provides practice with the sound of **/kw/** for **qu**. Help your child name the pictures and practice writing the letters.

Name

Phonemic Awareness

● Say the name of each picture.
Circle the pictures that begin with the same sound as **ring**.

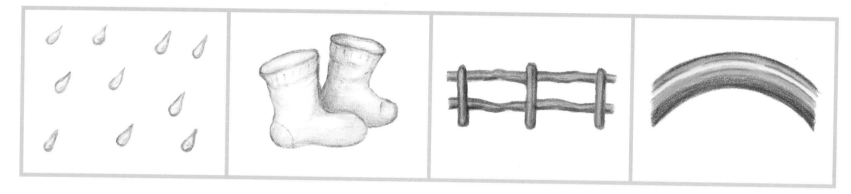

Sound-Symbol Awareness

★ Read the name of each picture.
Circle each **r**.

rain   rocks    rake

To the Teacher
Help children recognize the **/r/** sound as they name each picture. Associate this sound with the letters **Rr**.

▲ Trace. Practice.

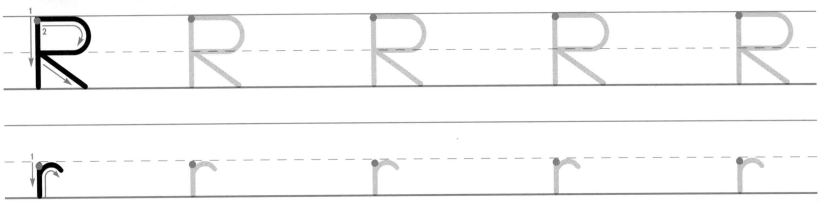

Spelling Awareness

■ Write **r** to complete each spelling.

  ing

  ed

 ose

  ake

Name _____

S s

● Say the name of each picture.
Circle the pictures that begin with the same sound as **6 six**.

★ Read the name of each picture.
Circle each **s**.

six

seal

shell

To the Teacher
Help children recognize the **/s/** sound as they name each picture. Associate this sound with the letters **Ss**.

▲ Trace. Practice.

S S S S S

s s s s s

Spelling Awareness

■ Write **s** to complete each spelling.

 un

 ee

 and

 nail

School/Home
This page provides practice with the sound of initial **Ss**. Help your child name the pictures and practice writing the letters.

Name

Phonemic Awareness

● Say the name of each picture.
  Circle the pictures that begin with the same sound as 🏕 **tent**.

Sound-Symbol Awareness

★ Say the name of each picture as you read.
  Circle each **T** and **t**.

 Teddy bear, teddy bear, turn around.

 To the Teacher
Help children recognize the /t/ sound as they name each picture. Associate this sound with the letters **Tt**.

▲ Trace. Practice.

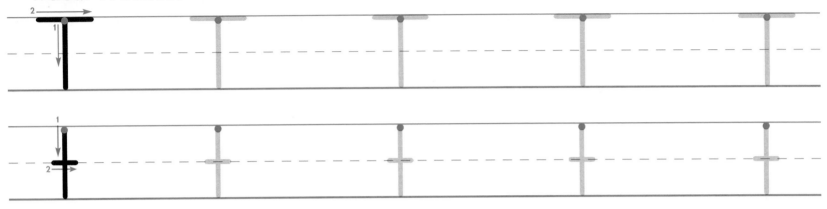

Spelling Awareness

■ Write **t** to complete each spelling.

 en

 ime

 ools

 op

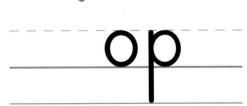

School/Home
This page provides practice with the sound of initial **Tt**. Help your child name the pictures and practice writing the letters.

Name _____

Phonemic Awareness

● Say the name of each picture.
Circle the pictures that begin with the same sound as **umbrellas**.

Sound-Symbol Awareness

★ Say the name of the picture as you read.
Circle each **u**.

The tulips hold  umbrellas upside down!

 To the Teacher
Help children recognize the **short u** sound as they name each picture. Associate this sound with the letters **Uu**.

▲ Trace. Practice.

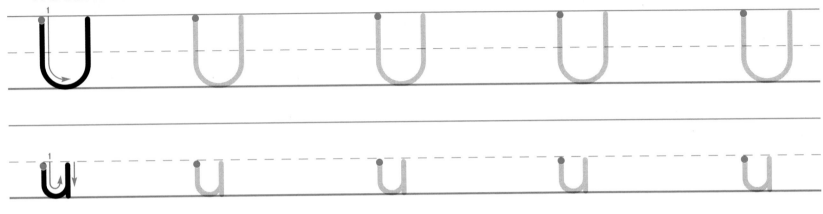

Spelling Awareness

■ Write **u** to complete each spelling.

   p

   nder

   s

   b g

School/Home
This page provides practice with the sound of **short u**. Help your child name the pictures and practice writing the letters.

Phonemic Awareness

● Say the name of each picture.
Circle the pictures that begin with the same sound as  **vase**.

Sound-Symbol Awareness

★ Say the name of the picture as you read.
Circle each **v**.

Be my very special

 valentine.

Letter Awareness

▲ Trace. Practice.

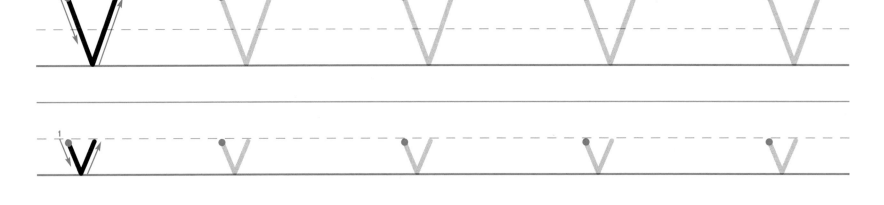

Spelling Awareness

■ Write **v** to complete each spelling.

  an

  ery

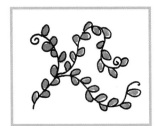  ine

  est

48

  School/Home
This page provides practice with the sound of initial **Vv**. Help your child name the pictures and practice writing the letters.

Name

Phonemic Awareness

● Say the name of each picture.
Circle the pictures that begin with the same sound as ～ **worm**.

Sound-Symbol Awareness

★ Read the name of each picture.
Circle each **w**.

water   wagon   woods

To the Teacher
Help children recognize the /w/ sound as they name each picture. Associate this sound with the letters **Ww**.

49

▲ Trace. Practice.

Spelling Awareness

■ Write **w** to complete each spelling.

  eb

  hat

  ater

  ing

School/Home
This page provides practice with the sound of initial **Ww**. Help your child name the pictures and practice writing the letters.

Name

Phonemic Awareness

● Say the name of each picture.
Circle the pictures that end with the same sound as **6 six**.

Sound-Symbol Awareness

★ Read the name of each picture.
Circle each **x**.

fox　　　　　ox　　　　　six

To the Teacher
Help children recognize the **/ks/** sound as they name each picture. Associate this sound with the letters **Xx**.

Letter Awareness

▲ Trace. Practice.

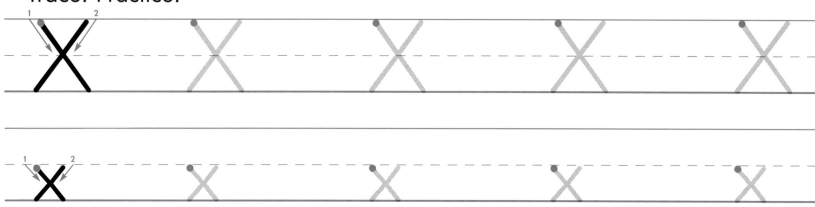

Spelling Awareness

■ Write **x** to complete each spelling.

  bo

  e it

  a

  mi

School/Home
This page provides practice with the sound of **/ks/**. Help your child name the pictures and practice writing the letters.

Name

Phonemic Awareness

● Say the name of each picture.
Circle the pictures that begin with the same sound as **yo-yo**.

Sound-Symbol Awareness

★ Read the name of each picture.
Circle each **y**.

yawn   yo-yo   yarn

To the Teacher
Help children recognize the **/y/** sound as they name each picture. Associate this sound with the letters **Yy**.

▲ Trace. Practice.

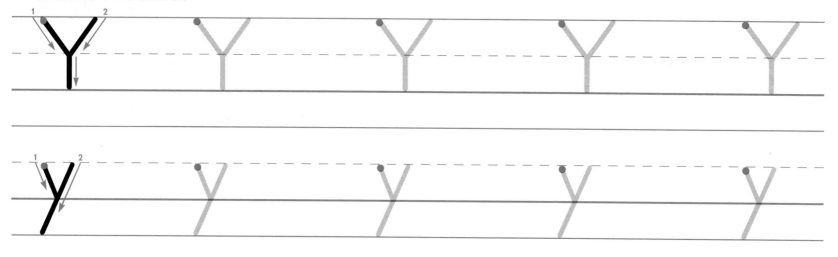

Spelling Awareness

■ Write **y** to complete each spelling.

 ellow

 es

 o- o

 ell

 **School/Home**
This page provides practice with the sound of initial **Yy**. Help your child name the pictures and practice writing the letters.

Name _____

Phonemic Awareness

● Say the name of each picture.
Circle the pictures that begin with the same sound as 🦓 **zebra**.

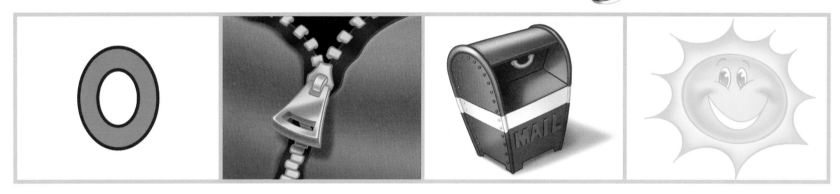

Sound-Symbol Awareness

★ Say the name of each picture as you read.
Circle each **z**.

The  zebra ⧩ zigzags all the way!

To the Teacher
Help children recognize the /**z**/ sound as they name each picture. Associate this sound with the letters **Zz**.

▲ Trace. Practice.

Z Z Z Z Z Z

z z z z z z

Spelling Awareness

■ Write **z** to complete each spelling.

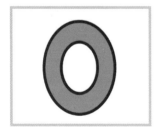 ero

 bu

 oo

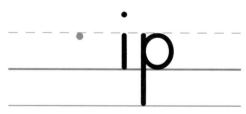 ip

School/Home
This page provides practice with the sound of **Zz**. Help your child name the pictures and practice writing the letters.

My Words

A a

B b

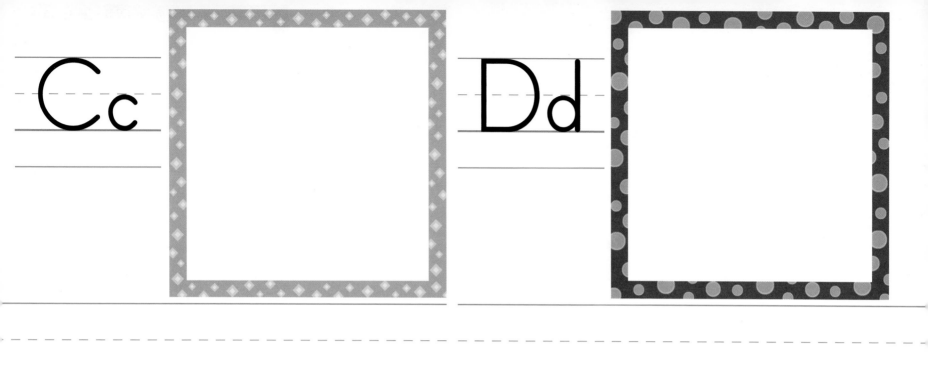

C c

D d

E e

F f

Gg

Hh

Ii

Jj

Kk

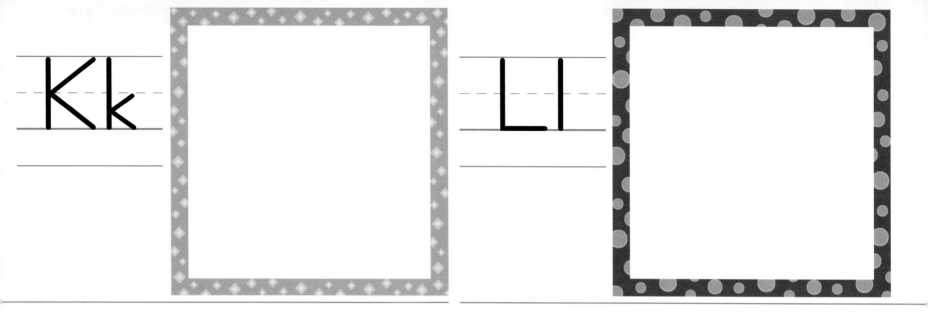

Ll

Mm

Nn

Oo

Pp

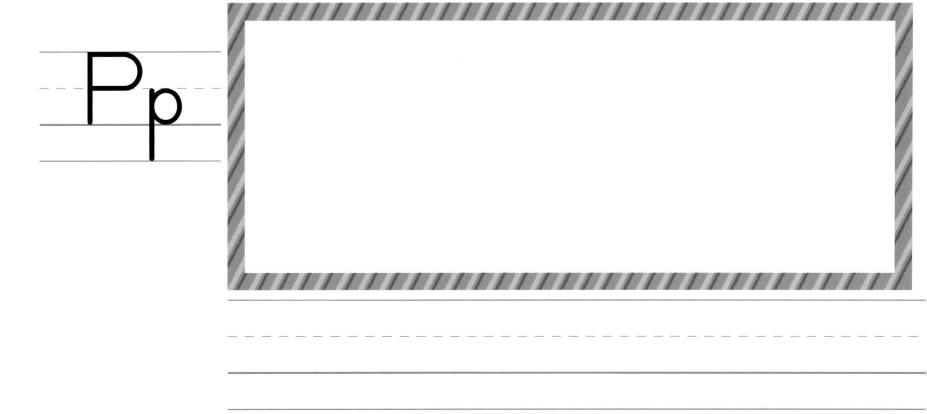

Qq

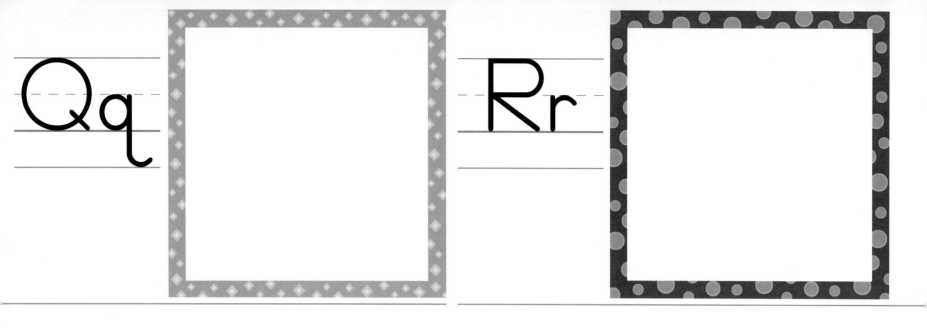

Rr

Ss

T t

U u

V v

Ww

Xx

Yy

Zz